Heart 2 HEART

Welcome to
YOUR *dazzling*
TWO-WAY BOOK
and **JOURNAL!**

Fill this half of the book with your
hopes, dreams and **heart's desires.**
Flip the book over to find your
very own journal.

*make
believe
ideas*

I LOVE TO BE me!

Being me is wonderful – nobody does it better!

My name: ....

I rate my name .... **/10**

Other names I like to be called:
....

My birthday: ....

My age today is .... years .... months .... days.

The place I was born: ....

The time I was born: ....

Tape a picture of yourself here.

Choose one word from each side of the heart, then combine these to create your fame name.

Violet   Ocean
Matty   Kelly   Zara
Billie   Charlie   Louie
Liberty   Alex
Taylor   Tabby
Brooke
Edie
Bear

Star   Sparkle
Dazzle-Dew   Diamond
Appleton   Pickle   Berry
Frost   Valentine
Summer
Grace
Heath   Winter
Peardrop
Rose

My fame name:
....

What I'd love to be famous for:
....

My birthstone

Circle the birthstone for the month you were born.

January
Garnet

February
Amethyst

March
Aquamarine

April
Diamond

May
Emerald

June
Pearl

July
Ruby

August
Peridot

September
Sapphire

October
Opal

November
Citrine

December
Blue topaz

The five best things about me:

1. ....
2. ....
3. ....
4. ....
5. ....

My eye colour: ....
My hair colour: ....
My height: ....
My shoe size: ....

A little-known fact about me:
....

I ♥ me!

Where I live:
....

The people I live with:
....
....

My favourite place in the entire world is:
....

My favourite day of the year is:
....
because...
....
....

My favourite day of the week is:
....
because...
....
....

A drawing of my home

Five things I love about the people I live with:

1 ....
2 ....
3 ....
4 ....
5 ....

MY PERFECT day

Three people I'd like to share
my perfect day with:

1 ....

2 ....

3 ....

 At 9 o'clock ...
....
....
....

 At 11 o'clock ...
....
....
....

 At 1 o'clock ...
....
....
....

 At 3 o'clock ...
....
....
....

 At 5 o'clock ...
....
....
....

 At 7 o'clock ...
....
....
....

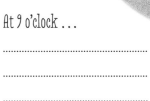
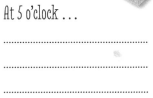

THE COLOUR OF MY *heart*

Tick the five hearts that contain the things you like best. Next, note which colour you have chosen more of to see what the colour of your heart says about you!

Reading

Choir

Practical jokes

Films

Puzzles

Crafts

Girl Guides

Drama club

Shopping

Sleepovers

Swimming

Poetry

After-school clubs

Concerts

Volunteering

Playing an instrument

Team sports

Parties

Camping

Keeping a diary

Dancing

Dog walking

Drawing

Theme parks

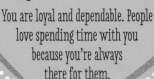

pink hearts than any other:

You are loyal and dependable. People love spending time with you because you're always there for them.

purple hearts than any other:

You are adventurous and always think of fun things to do. You can make anyone smile and are the life of any party.

blue hearts than any other:

You are caring, creative and like nothing more than giving thoughtful gifts, especially ones you made yourself. You can also write great stories and songs.

If you end up with two hearts of one colour and two of another, choose the word that best describes you and use the colour of its heart to reveal the colour of your heart.

ways to my *heart*

Tick your choices in the circles.

Do you prefer . . .

⭘ popcorn	OR	chocolate ⭘
⭘ strawberries	OR	bananas ⭘
⭘ hashtags	OR	emotis ⭘
⭘ kittens	OR	tigers ⭘
⭘ pool	OR	beach ⭘
⭘ dancing	OR	singing ⭘
⭘ sleepovers	OR	cinema ⭘
⭘ fruit	OR	vegetables ⭘
⭘ ocean view	OR	mountain view ⭘
⭘ skiing	OR	snorkelling ⭘
⭘ shopping for clothes	OR	shopping for gadgets ⭘
⭘ crafting	OR	playing sport ⭘

I  ALL ABOUT ME

5 words to describe me:
- ....
- ....
- ....
- ....
- ....

5 people I admire:
- ....
- ....
- ....
- ....
- ....

5 things I'm grateful for:
- ....
- ....
- ....
- ....
- ....

5 happy memories:
- ....
- ....
- ....
- ....
- ....

5 people I would share
my secrets with:
- ....
- ....
- ....
- ....
- ....

5 top hobbies:
- ....
- ....
- ....
- ....
- ....

TREE of

hearts

my family

Fill the leaves with the names
of your **family members**. If you like,
include the names of all the **people you
live with**, as well as your **pets**.

Fill in these pages with a friend.
Write your names, and then
take turns completing the quiz.

Heart 2

Name:

Oldest person in my family
....

Person with the most unusual talent
....

Sportiest person
....

Funniest person
....

Person with the most unusual name
....

Best dancer
....

Oldest pet in my family
....

The person I am most like
....

HEART my family

Oldest person in my family

....

Person with the most unusual talent

....

Sportiest person

....

Funniest person

....

Person with the most unusual name

....

Best dancer

....

Oldest pet in my family

....

The person I am most like

....

Name:

never have we ever

Complete this quiz with a friend. Each time you answer **yes to a question**, draw a heart in the box below your name. **Count your hearts**, and write your total at the bottom. The **more similar** you and your friend's results, the **more you have in common**.

Have you ever . . .

	Name	Name
been to a pop concert?		
visited another country?		
stayed awake all night?		
been on a boat?		
gone surfing?		
been on safari?		
worn a ball gown?		
stayed at a hotel?		
knitted a hat?		
sung in a play?		
seen a real crocodile?		
met a celebrity?		
watched a 3-D film?		
TOTAL:		

heartart

A STRING OF HEARTS

Make a pretty string of hearts
to decorate your room.

You will need:

- Scissors
- Red paper
- A pencil
- Thread or string
- Clear tape

1. Cut out 8 pieces of stiff red paper, approximately 8 cm x 8 cm (3 in x 3 in). Fold them in half. Draw half a heart on each one and then a smaller half-heart inside it.

2. Cut out the big and small hearts.

3. Tape some thread along the fold of a large heart. Then add the other large hearts to the same thread.

4. Tape a small heart in the centre of each large heart.

5. Write some of the things you love on the big hearts. These could be people, places, possessions, TV shows, food or anything else!

ways to my *heart*

Tick your choices in the circles.

Do you prefer . . .

- ○ smart **OR** casual ○
- ○ jumper **OR** vest top ○
- ○ bunches **OR** plaits ○
- ○ glitter **OR** sequins ○
- ○ stripes **OR** polka dots ○
- ○ pastel **OR** neon ○
- ○ sandals **OR** flip-flops ○
- ○ baseball cap **OR** beanie hat ○
- ○ tote bag **OR** handbag ○
- ○ scarves **OR** turtlenecks ○
- ○ gloves **OR** mittens ○
- ○ high heels **OR** trainers ○

I  FASHION

5 most-loved things in my wardrobe:

- ....
- ....
- ....
- ....
- ....

5 favourite accessories:

- ....
- ....
- ....
- ....
- ....

5 top hairstyles:

- ....
- ....
- ....
- ....
- ....

My dream party outfit would look like this.

Fill in these pages with a friend.
Write your names, and then
take turns completing the quiz.

Heart 2

Name:

Best class
....

Best after-school activity
....

Favourite teacher
....

Favourite thing about school
....

One thing I would change about school
....

Lunch meal I like best
....

Funniest thing I ever saw at school
....

My best moment
....

HEART my school

Best class

....

Best after-school activity

....

Favourite teacher

....

Favourite thing about school

....

One thing I would change about school

....

Lunch meal I like best

....

Funniest thing I ever saw at school

....

My best moment

....

Name:

TREE OF hearts

my friends

Fill the leaves with the
names of your friends and
other **people you like.**

ways to my *heart*

Tick your choices in the circles.

○ to study French **OR** to study Spanish ○

○ to start school at 6 a.m. **OR** to finish school at 6 p.m. ○

○ to have a weeklong science class **OR** to have a weeklong art class ○

○ to have a sandwich for lunch everyday **OR** to have a burger for lunch everyday ○

○ if science class was cancelled **OR** if music class was cancelled ○

○ to be the head teacher **OR** to be a teacher ○

○ to work in a group **OR** to work alone ○

○ to be a top student **OR** to be a sports star ○

○ to go to a school for the arts **OR** to go to a school for geniuses ○

○ to be the smartest in your class **OR** to be the funniest in your class ○

○ to wear a tracksuit to school **OR** to wear a suit to school ○

○ to learn to sing **OR** to learn to dance ○

Would you prefer . . . .

I  MY HEART'S DESIRES

These are my favourite things:

Person
....

Snack
....

Season
....

Book
....

Colour
....

Film
....

Song
....

Animal
....

Country
....

School subject
....

Fill in these pages with a friend. Write your names, and then take turns completing the quiz.

If you were stranded on a desert island and could only have one thing from each category, what would you choose?

Heart 2

Name:

Item from your bedroom
....

Item of furniture
....

Item from your kitchen
....

Electronic item
....

Book
....

Game
....

Outfit accessory
....

Food treat
....

HEART desert-island dreams

Item from your bedroom
....

Item of furniture
....

Item from your kitchen
....

Electronic item
....

Book
....

Game
....

Outfit accessory
....

Food treat
....

Name:

TREE OF hearts

the most *wonderful times* of the year

Fill the leaves with **the birthdays,**
celebrations and other times of the year
that are **closest to your heart.**

ways to my *heart*

Tick your choices in the circles.

Would you prefer . . .

◯ surfing	OR	snowboarding ◯
◯ running	OR	cycling ◯
◯ an apartment	OR	a hotel ◯
◯ swimming	OR	sailing ◯
◯ summer	OR	winter ◯
◯ to travel the world	OR	to travel into space ◯
◯ a city break	OR	a country retreat ◯
◯ a safari	OR	mountain hiking ◯
◯ a ship	OR	an aeroplane ◯
◯ swimming with dolphins	OR	snorkelling with turtles ◯
◯ to zip line over a forest	OR	to scuba dive ◯
◯ to stay in an arctic igloo	OR	to stay in a tropical treehouse ◯

 **MY BUCKET LIST**

5 places I'd like to visit:

- ....
- ....
- ....
- ....
- ....

5 sports I'd like to learn:

- ....
- ....
- ....
- ....
- ....

5 activities I'd like to try:

- ....
- ....
- ....
- ....
- ....

5 films I'd like to see:

- ....
- ....
- ....
- ....
- ....

5 people I'd like to meet:

- ....
- ....
- ....
- ....
- ....

5 skills I'd like to learn:

- ....
- ....
- ....
- ....
- ....

Fill in these pages with a friend.
Write your names, and then
take turns completing the quiz.

Heart 2

Name:

Name I would choose if I had to change mine

....

Favourite celebrity

....

Best gift I've ever received

....

An animal I would like to be

....

Most embarrassing moment at school

....

A book character I would love to have as a friend

....

The silliest excuse I have ever given

....

My funniest habit

....

HEART fun secrets

Name I would choose if I had to change mine
....

Favourite celebrity
....

Best gift I've ever received
....

An animal I would like to be
....

Most embarrassing moment at school
....

A book character I would love to have as a friend
....

The silliest excuse I have ever given
....

My funniest habit
....

Name:

TREE OF hearts

my favourite places in the world

Fill the leaves with the names of the **countries, towns, cities** and **places** you **love the most.**

heart**art**

JAR OF HEARTS

Fill a jar with secret notes about the things you love. They could be people, places, memories or anything else. Then, every time you discover something new that you love, add another note to your jar.

You will need:

- Scissors
- A pencil
- A jar
- Decorations for your jar

1. Carefully cut out the mini notes on the next three pages of this book.

2. Write one thing that you love on each note. It might be your pet or an activity you love to do on the weekends.

3. After writing each note, roll it up and tuck it into your jar for safekeeping.

4. Decorate the jar with ribbons, hearts, glitter and anything else you like.

I love . . .

I like . . .

This page and the next two pages contain the mini notes needed for your jar of hearts.

I  MY YEAR

5 best summer activities:

5 funny memories:

5 best winter activities:

5 special occasions this year:

5 top weekend activities:

5 best friends:

Fill in these pages with a friend.
Write your names, and then
take turns completing the quiz.

Heart 2

Name:

Furthest place I've ever travelled to

....

Latest bedtime

....

Earliest morning

....

Longest car journey

....

Greatest school achievement

....

Longest phone call

....

Tastiest food I ever ate

....

Longest time away from home

....

HEART extremes

Furthest place I've ever travelled to
....

Latest bedtime
....

Earliest morning
....

Longest car journey
....

Greatest school achievement
....

Longest phone call
....

Tastiest food I ever ate
....

Longest time away from home
....

Name:

never
have we
ever

Complete this quiz with a friend. Each time you answer **yes to a question, draw a heart** in the box below your name. **Count your hearts**, and write your total at the bottom. The **more similar** you and your friend's results, the **more you have in common**.

Have you ever . . .

	Name	Name
learnt to play the piano?		
volunteered for charity?		
painted a portrait?		
been on a plane?		
eaten escargot? (snails)		
written a song?		
sung in the shower?		
been in a hot-air balloon?		
knitted a scarf?		
watched TV all day?		
got an A for a school assignment?		
run a mile?		
owned a pet?		
TOTAL:		

SUPER
Secret
POCKET

WELCOME to YOUR SUPER *Secret* POCKET!

Carefully **cut along the dotted line,** and then **tape the pages together.**

Now you have a special pocket for storing your **secret notes.**

Make sure you **fix the top of the pocket with a paperclip** before you flip the book over.

TAPE HERE

TAPE HERE

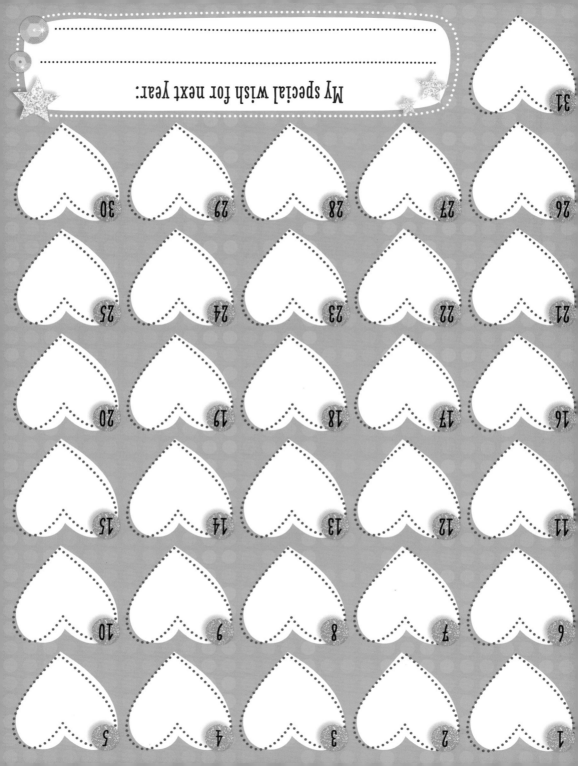

My special wish for next year:

December

Three things I'm looking
forward to this month:

1

2

3

Three things I loved
about this month:

1

2

3

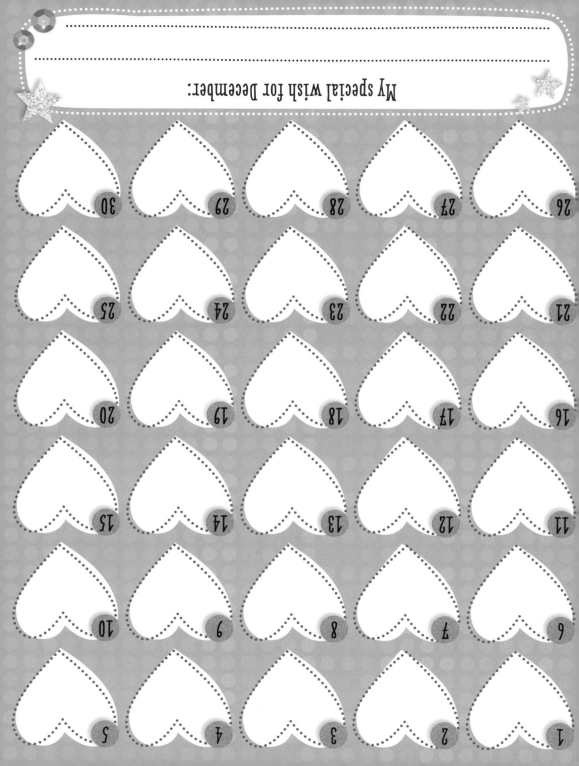

My special wish for December:

30 29 28 27 26

25 24 23 22 21

20 19 18 17 16

15 14 13 12 11

10 9 8 7 6

5 4 3 2 1

November

Three things I'm looking
forward to this month:

1

2

3

Three things I loved
about this month:

1

2

3

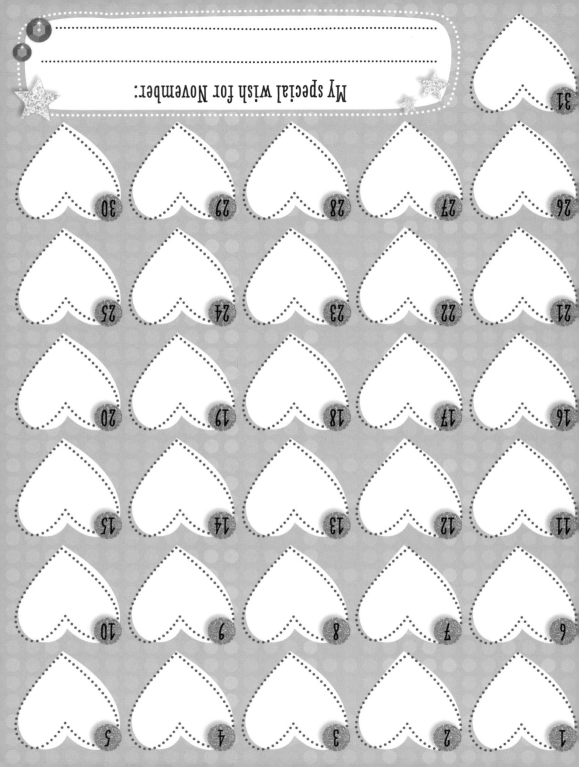

My special wish for November:

October

Three things I'm looking forward to this month:

1.
2.
3.

Three things I loved about this month:

1.
2.
3.

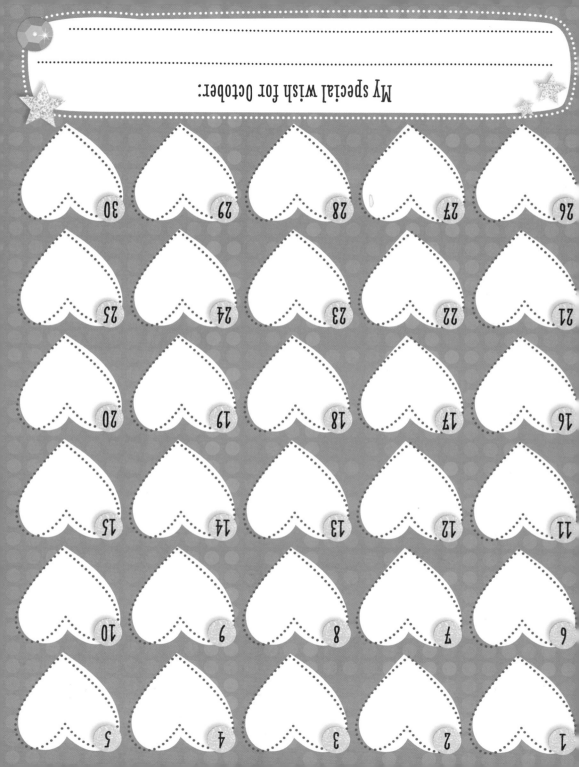

My special wish for October:

Three things I loved
about this month:

1

2

3

_____

_____

_____

Three things I'm looking
forward to this month:

1

2

3

_____

_____

_____

September

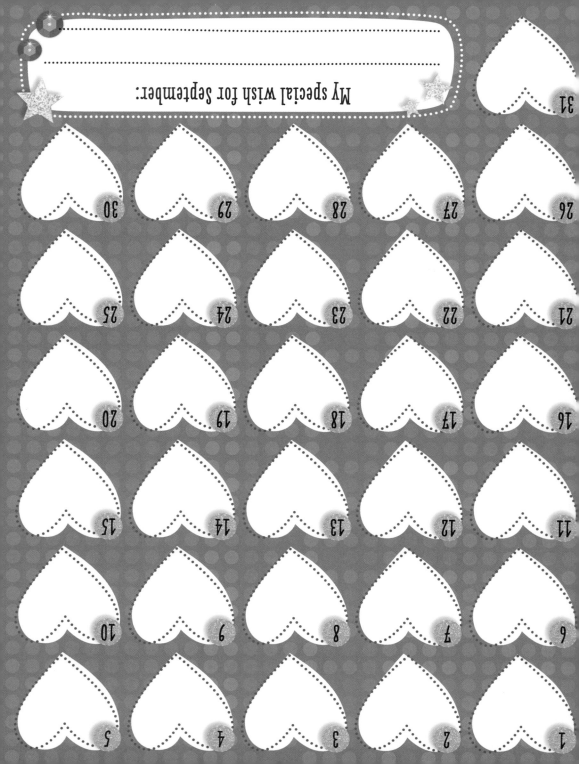

My special wish for September:

August

Three things I'm looking forward to this month:

1 ....
2 ....
3 ....

Three things I loved about this month:

1 ....
2 ....
3 ....

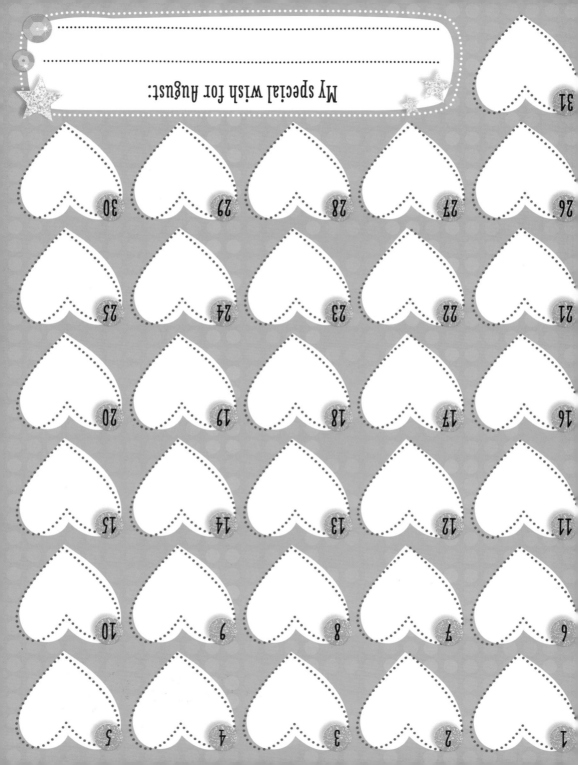

My special wish for August:

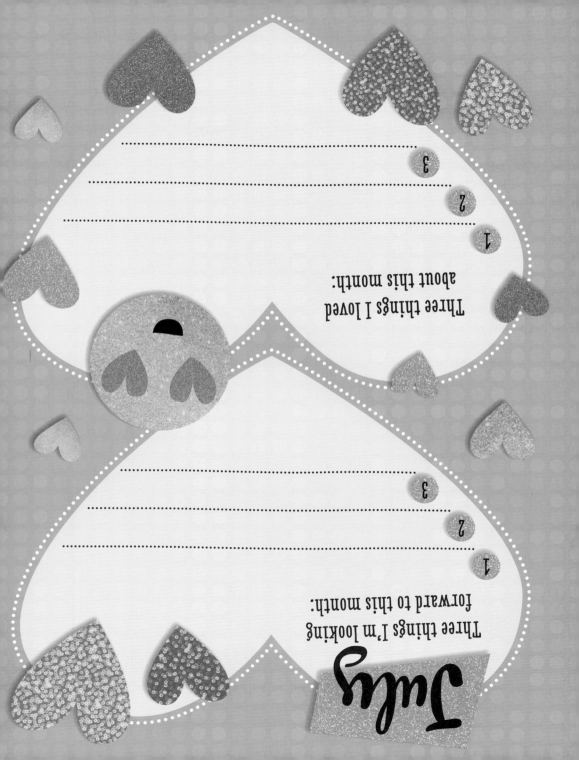

July

Three things I'm looking
forward to this month:

1
2
3

Three things I loved
about this month:

1
2
3

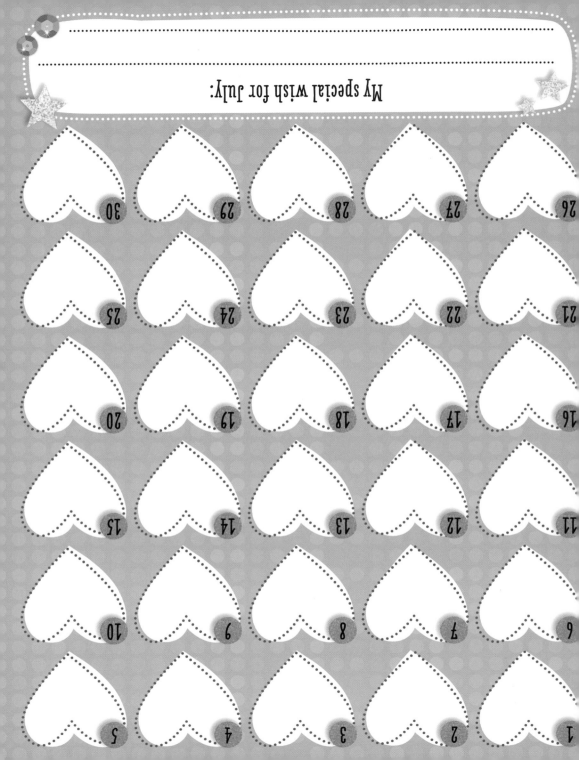

My special wish for July:

30 29 28 27 26

25 24 23 22 21

20 19 18 17 16

15 14 13 12 11

10 9 8 7 6

5 4 3 2 1

June

Three things I loved about this month:

1. ....
2. ....
3. ....

Three things I'm looking forward to this month:

1. ....
2. ....
3. ....

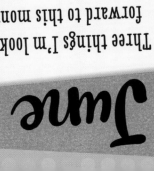

My special wish for June:

31
30 29 28 27 26
25 24 23 22 21
20 19 18 17 16
15 14 13 12 11
10 9 8 7 6
5 4 3 2 1

Three things I loved
about this month:

1
2
3

Three things I'm looking
forward to this month:

1
2
3

May

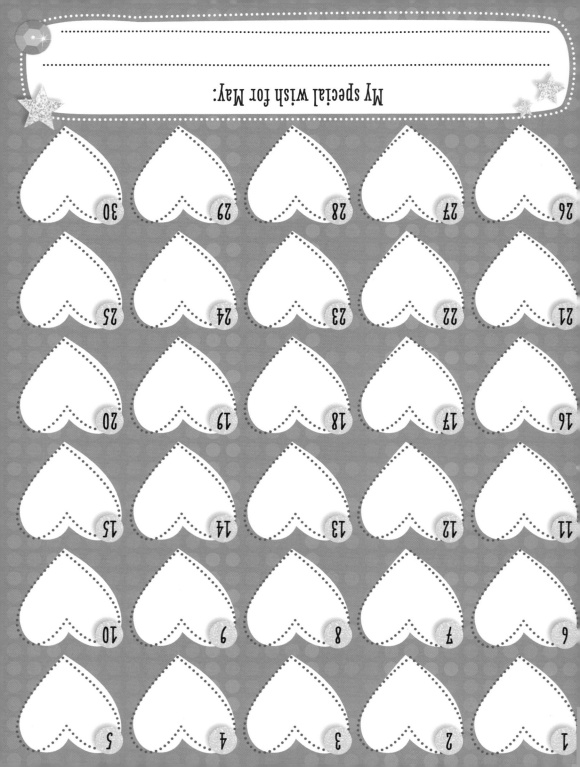

My special wish for May:

30 29 28 27 26

25 24 23 22 21

20 19 18 17 16

15 14 13 12 11

10 9 8 7 6

5 4 3 2 1

Three things I loved
about this month:

1

2

3

Three things I'm looking
forward to this month:

1

2

3

April

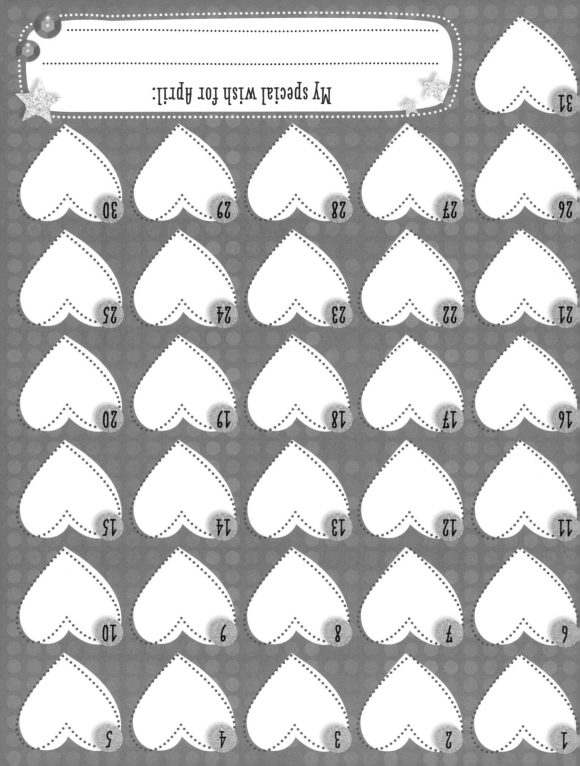

My special wish for April:

March

Three things I'm looking forward to this month:

1
2
3

....

....

....

Three things I loved about this month:

1
2
3

....

....

....

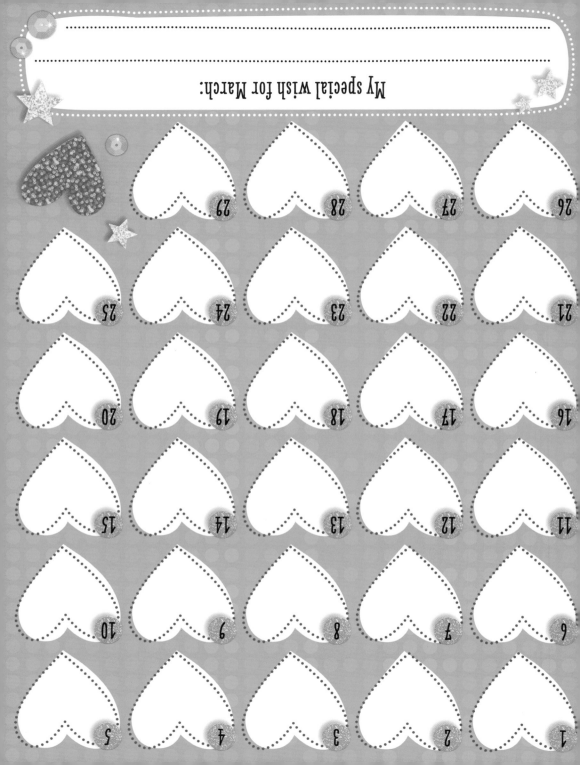

My special wish for March:

February

Three things I'm looking
forward to this month:

1

2

3

_____

_____

_____

Three things I loved
about this month:

1

2

3

_____

_____

_____

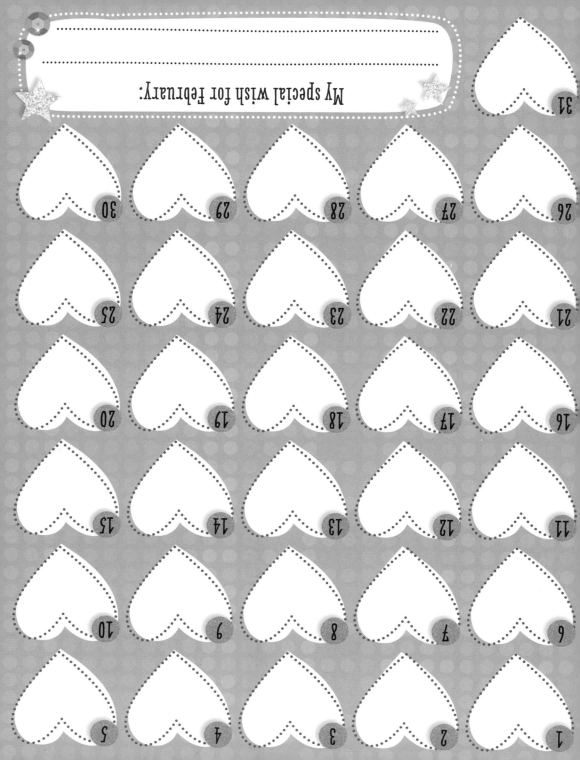

My special wish for February:

January

Three things I'm looking forward to this month:

1 ....
2 ....
3 ....

Three things I loved about this month:

1 ....
2 ....
3 ....

Heart 2 HEART JOURNAL

For each month, there are two hearts on the left-hand page.
Fill in the first heart at the start of the month,
and fill in the second heart at the end of the month.

♥ ♥ ♥

Ways you could fill in the daily hearts:
• Record any fun or important things that are planned.
• Jot down what happened each day and how you feel about it.

1
Gym starts today!

30
Mia is my new BFF!